ICRF 12

KU-359-091

BEASTS ON THE HOOF

Even-toed ungulates

The even-toed ungulates such as cattle and deer resemble their odd-toed cousins, for they have evolved in similar ways to suit the same environmental pressures. Most are grazing or browsing animals, spending much of their time out on the open grasslands where the best defence against predators is the ability to run fast. Their limbs, therefore, have become adapted for speed, like those of the horse.

There are differences between the two groups, however, which are not restricted to their feet. Even-toed ungulates often have well-developed and complex glandular systems that produce a range of scent signals important for communication within social groups. Many species have horns or antlers ranging from the simple knobs of the giraffe to the elaborate, multi-branched antlers of the moose.

Cattle, deer and other even-toed ungulates have spread throughout the world. They have diversified into a large number of distinct species, each suited to a particular way of life. While the odd-toed ungulates are dwindling in variety, the even-toed forms are flourishing (there are 187 species of the latter compared to 16 of the former). This contrasts with much of the ungulates' evolutionary history when the odd-toed were the dominant group. Their decline is probably due more to climatic factors than to direct competition with even-toed ungulates.

Over two-thirds of domestic animals are even-toed ungulates. Selective breeding has created innumerable varieties of some species - notably cattle, sheep and pigs. Many of these varieties, or breeds, have been developed to suit environments that their wild ancestors were unable to colonize, and this has extended the range of this group still further.

All even-toed ungulates belong to a single order - the Artiodactyla or artiodactyls. This is divided into two major categories: the non-ruminants and the ruminants (the second group includes the suborder Tylopoda, the camels).

Pigs and hippos

The non-ruminants include the pigs, peccaries and hippopotamuses. They are all four-toed animals with thick-set bodies and almost non-existent necks. They also have comparatively short legs. Although some

ABOVE One of the most primitive of all large mammals, the tapir has managed to keep its head above water for some 20 million years. This Malayan tapir lives in the dense jungles of South-east Asia, where it browses on leaves using its short mobile trunk. It is an excellent swimmer and will escape from tigers and leopards by diving into the water and remaining submerged for several minutes. **PAGES 302 AND 303** Rival males skirmishing at a hippopotamus wallow.

species, such as the wild boar, are swift and agile, most of them do not rely on speed to escape their enemies. Pigs and peccaries rely on their ability to vanish into the forest undergrowth, while hippos rely on their intimidating size and the protection offered by their aquatic way of life. Both pigs and hippos are also equipped with sharp tusks that are able to cause serious harm to an attacker.

Compared with many grazing animals the pigs and peccaries have simple digestive systems that are not built to digest large amounts of tough grass. Instead, the animals eat a wider range of foods, including insects and carrion. This broader diet means that their teeth are relatively unspecialized. Unlike most other ungulates they have well-developed canines. Many pigs, such as warthogs, have long upward-pointing canines that grow into prominent tusks.

Hippopotamuses feed mainly on grass. Despite this their digestive systems are quite primitive and pig-like. They digest their food in a compartmented stomach inhabited by micro-organisms - bacteria and minute animals (protozoa) - that ferment the grass and convert the cellulose to sugars. This works well enough for the hippopotamus, but the food passes through the gut too quickly for complete fermentation, and much of the food value is wasted.

The camel family occupies arid regions stretching across North Africa, Asia and the western length of South America.

Camels and llamas

The tylopods, or camels and llamas, are two-toed ungulates whose feet have become adapted for life in arid habitats. Their body weight does not rest on hooves; instead they have large fleshy sole-pads that spread the load and prevent them from sinking into the soft sand of the desert areas they live in.

Both llamas and camels are agile, fast-moving creatures that burn a lot of energy. To replace this lost energy from dry grasses and thorny bushes, they have evolved a digestive system that breaks down the cellulose of the plant's cell walls, and allows the digestive juices to work on the cell's carbohydrates and proteins.

After fermenting in a three-chambered stomach the food is regurgitated in small quantities to be chewed over a second time. This is known as 'chewing the cud'. The second chewing hastens the breakdown process, and when swallowed again the food is ready to be attacked by the digestive juices.

Cattle, sheep and deer

The ruminants have taken the principle of cud-chewing even further. They have evolved complex, four-chambered digestive systems that give the bacteria and protozoa the chance to break down the cellulose over a long period. The initial fermentation occurs in a large stomach chamber called the rumen, which has been filled with food during a bout of intense grazing. Having 'stewed' for a while in the rumen the food is regurgitated to be chewed properly, then swallowed again. The second time round it bypasses the rumen, and enters a further series of digestion chambers - the reticulum, omasum and abomasum - where the micro-organisms continue their work.

The ability to fill the rumen quickly, and chew the contents at leisure, gives ruminants a big advantage over other grazing animals, for herbivores are especially vulnerable to their enemies when feeding on the open grasslands. Non-ruminants such as horses and zebras need to graze at a steady rate for long periods, and they often rely on the vigilance of 'sentries' while the rest of the herd feeds. By contrast, a ruminant can quickly store the necessary food without chewing it properly, then find a place away from the open grazing grounds to chew the cud in safety.

Deer, giraffes, antelopes, cattle, sheep, and goats are all ruminants. Many of these, particularly the males, have horns or antlers. Horns are permanent bony extensions of the skull. The solid antlers of deer are also bony outgrowths of the skull but are unique in that they are shed and replaced each season. While the antlers are growing they are covered in 'velvet'.- a layer of fine-furred skin containing a network of blood vessels that supply the developing bone below. Once the bone is fully formed the blood supply is cut off and the velvet comes away. The antlers are now dead, like hair or the tips of fingernails. In this condition they make excellent weapons for settling disputes between rival males. Once the mating season is over, the antlers fall away, and the whole process begins all over again the following season.

The giraffe must be one of the most distinctive of all mammals. It, too, is a ruminant, and browses for leaves on the tall trees of the open savannah. Over the years natural selection has favoured animals that could reach the higher foliage growing above the level accessible to grazing animals, and as a result the giraffe has developed into a specialized upper-storey feeder. Its close relative, the okapi, lives in forests, where there is plenty to eat much nearer ground level; consequently it has not developed in the same way as giraffes and probably looks very like the giraffe's short-necked ancestors. Both giraffes and okapis have small, permanent skin-covered horns.

SUB-UNGULATES CLASSIFICATION

The sub-ungulates consist of four orders that have evolved from the primitive ancestors of the ungulates (hoofed mammals). They do not have hooves, since they became separated from the mainstream of ungulate evolution before the hoof was developed.

The first order to diverge from the mainstream was the Tubulidentata. Today only one species belonging to this order survives: the aardvark *Orycteropus afer*, found throughout much of Africa south of the Sahara.

The other three orders are more closely related, having evolved from a single group that split off from the mainstream later than the ancestors of the aardvark. They are the elephants of the order Proboscidea, the hyraxes of the order Hyracoidea. and the sea cows of the order Sirenia.

ABOVE **A family of wild boar piglets trot behind their bristly parent as she picks her way across a forest track. Pigs have a much broader diet than other ungulates, eating ferns, roots, bulbs, insects, frogs and** nestlings. **This adult may well be looking for insects or carrion.**
RIGHT **Perched up a tree in the African rain forest, the western tree hyrax looks more like a large rat than an animal that shares an ancestor with elephants.**

Of all the ruminants, the cattle, sheep, goats and antelopes of the family Bovidae are the most successful, to judge by the number of species. The bovids, as they are often called, are represented throughout the world except for South America and Australia (although man has introduced them to Australia). They include species adapted to every climate and habitat - including deserts, tropical forests, temperate grasslands, Arctic tundra and the highest mountains. Because of this many of the bovids have been domesticated and introduced to areas that they would probably never have colonized on their own.

The horns of cattle, sheep and antelopes are permanent, and consist of bony cores sheathed in hardened and thickened skin to form a hoof-like material. In some species, such as the pronghorn, the horny outer covering is shed each year to leave room for new growth.

ABOVE Horn to horn, two anoa antelopes settle a difference with a brief fencing match. The ridges on their horns may be an adaptation to lock the horns together on contact; this would prevent them slipping sideways and causing real damage. It is much better if disputes can be settled by a trial of strength, rather than by inflicting serious injuries that might well prove to be fatal.

BELOW The stomach of a ruminant is a complex organ designed to make the best of a diet of grass and leaves. The food enters the rumen (ru) where it is attacked by bacteria before being regurgitated up the oesophagus (es) to be chewed a second time. It is then swallowed again and passes to the reticulum (re), omasum (om), and abomasum (ab) for further digestion.

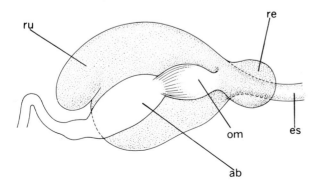

Horns and antlers - what are they for?

One of the most striking features of ungulates is that many of them - and the ruminants in particular - have horns or antlers. Often these are very long or complex structures, and in the case of deer they are shed and regrown each year, a process that uses up a good deal of energy. They are obviously important. If such heavy, apparently cumbersome and energy-absorbing structures were of little use, the processes of natural selection would have got rid of them long ago. So what are they for?

Since many ungulates are the prey of large carnivores, it is reasonable to suggest that they use their horns for defence. Certainly some ungulates have horns that prove formidable weapons against predators. The oryx can stab an attacking lion with its long horns, and a herd of musk oxen will defend themselves from a pack of wolves by forming a protective circle, heads down, their sharp horns pointing outwards like a ring of swords.

Yet, in many species, horns are rarely used against predators, and when they are they often turn out to be quite ineffective. In most deer only the males have antlers, but the females are no less subsceptible to attacks from carnivores. If antlers were a useful protection, we might expect them to be possessed by both sexes. Moreover, the males shed their antlers each year, and yet there is no reduction in predation pressure. The classic example is the reindeer, which loses its antlers in late winter and spring when the wolf, its main enemy, is most active.

Weapons of rivalry

From observation of ungulates in the wild, we now know that the main use of horns and antlers is to settle disputes between males of the same species, either to establish a ranking order or to claim and defend females.

The largest species generally have the most impressive horns or antlers. Examples are the African buffalo and the moose. Their head adornments are not merely bigger, as you would expect, but more complex. Smaller species tend to have much simpler horns. One possible reason for this is that small animals are more agile, and when they are fighting they will use a whole range of combat techniques: jumps, bites, kicks, and head-butts. Weapons on the head are only part of their arsenal. If a large animal tried all these techniques it would probably damage itself. An 800kg moose attempting to jump up and kick its opponent would probably pull a muscle or even break a leg. As a result big animals have tended to employ the technique that makes most use of sheer weight: the head-butt. Hence their weaponry has been concentrated on the head, where it is most effective.

Yet this created a new set of problems. Small ungulates - and probably the ancestors of large ones - tend to go for the unprotected flanks of their opponents, and may inflict severe injuries. Luckily a lightweight fighter with small horns rarely kills its opponent, but if a well-armed heavyweight used the same tactic it would almost certainly cause a mortal wound as soon as it made contact. Every fight would be to the death.It takes little imagination to see that for an animal population this could be disastrous. Fights are a daily occurrence among members of aggressive species. If each fight ends in a death, the animals will wipe each other out. Some sort of defence or counter-measure is essential.

Some species such as pigs, okapis and Rocky Mountain goats have developed thicker hide on their flanks to make it less vulnerable. Some have evolved inhibition mechanisms that prevent them striking each other too hard, and these are often linked to a hierarchy that ensures each animal knows its place. In

ABOVE Giraffes have perfected the art of ritualized combat. Disputing males stand flank to flank and take turns to hit at each other's neck and chest with the tips of their horns. In due course, one of the contestants concedes defeat, indicating his submission by a gesture, and the fight is called off. Such competitions make aggressive, potentially dangerous fighting unnecessary, and ensure that the species as a whole is not endangered by internal strife.

ABOVE **Many ungulates have permanent horns, but deer grow a new set every year. They start out as small knobs, then sprout short branches that gradually get longer as the season advances. As they grow, they are fed by a** network of blood vessels protected by a layer of fine-furred skin called velvet. This is scraped off when the antlers are fully-grown. Once the mating season is over the antlers fall off, and the process starts all over again.

such cases a subordinate member of the group will always give way to its superior, and a potentially dangerous fight is avoided. Many species, such as the nilgau, have developed a system of ritualized combat that falls short of any contact that could cause injury. Red deer stags engage in 'roaring' matches which often replace physical fighting altogether.

The simplest defence appears to have been the last to evolve: using head-butts to parry other head-butts. This tactic naturally favours animals with very solid, strong skulls, and horns that do not point forwards in lethal fashion - as they do in the case of the nilgau. The best equipment to have is a large skull with divergent horns, as possessed by the bisons and all true cattle. Such animals still go for one anothers' flanks, but defend themselves by parrying with their heads. The result is that they spend a lot of time head-to-head, each trying to get past and strike the other's flank.

Locked in combat

Many animals such as deer and bighorn sheep appear to have stopped trying to find a way to the flank, and simply go straight for the head. Since both skull and horns are reinforced this is relatively harmless. Nevertheless if they misjudge the charge and slip past each other the two adversaries could still cause considerable damage, and it may be that the complexity of a deer's antlers is a device to lock them together on contact and prevent them slipping sideways. The nodules and ornamentation on the horns of ibex and gazelles could serve the same purpose. In sheep the horns of mature males grow into a spiral, which is much less dangerous than a pointed horn. They always fight head on, and the clashes have a ritualized air: they are very deliberate and appear to be carried out in slow motion.

Horns are also used to impress. During fights the animals will sometimes taunt each other by exposing their flanks and flourishing their horns. Deer with complex antlers often dispense with the flank-showing and simply try to intimidate each other with a display of superiority. In such cases the antlers of a dominant animal undoubtedly help it to impose its supremacy on others. In many species such as red deer, ibex and bighorn sheep the antlers or horns become more impressive as the animal matures. Other individuals are probably aware of this, and tend to give way to animals with superior horns, before a true fight develops.

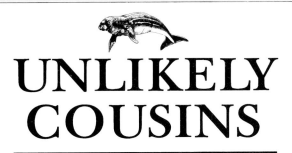

UNLIKELY COUSINS

Though strikingly different today, the aardvark, the hyraxes and the sirenians all evolved from the same ancestors of 65 million years ago

Some 65 million years ago the ancestors of the ungulates, know as the Condylarthra, produced offshoots that developed very differently from the hoofed mammals. They had no hooves, for they became separated from the ungulates long before hooves evolved, and some of them adopted very different ways of life. Over the years many became extinct, and today only 18 species of these 'primitive ungulates' survive. They are the aardvark, hyraxes, sea-cows and elephants.

A more unlikely band of relatives would be hard to find. The aardvark is a specialised nocturnal feeder on ants and termites, hyraxes look like rodents, and sea-cows are aquatic creatures that could easily be mistaken for seals. None of these animals bears the slightest resemblance to an elephant. Their common ancestry, and their connection with the ungulates, has been established only by careful examination of their teeth and bones. They are a striking example of the way one group of animals can split up and evolve in different ways to suit different environments.

Millions of years hunting insects

Fossil evidence suggests that the aardvark was already eating termites back in the Miocene period, over 20 million years ago, and it still eats them to this day. Because of this diet it has a lot in common with the anteaters and pangolins, although it is completely unrelated to them.

The aardvark is a humpbacked, long-eared, long-snouted burrowing creature that looks rather like a cross between a kangaroo and a pig. Yet despite its awkward appearance it is a most efficient animal, so well adapted to its way of life that it has changed little over all those millions of years.

It grows to the size of a small pig (it is sometimes known as the 'earth pig'), and usually weighs about 40 to 60kg. Its feet are quite unlike those of ungulates, with four toes at the front and five at the back, and they are provided with short, sturdy claws that make efficient excavating tools for breaking into termite mounds or digging deep burrows. To the zoologist the aardvark's most distinctive feature is its teeth: it has no incisors or canines, and tubular, peg-like cheek teeth. It is these that give the order Tubulidentata its name. The aardvark is its only member.

Tight fit

They are found through most of central and southern Africa except for desert areas, but they are so elusive that their burrows are often the only clue to their presence. These are up to 4m long and end in round chambers used as living quarters. The approach tunnel is quite narrow, and so closely moulded to the shape of the animal that it has to reach the living chamber before it can turn round. Hunters who have attempted to pull an aardvark out of its home have found that they may need the help of several people, for the animal braces its back against the walls and presses its feet and claws hard against the tunnel floor to wedge itself in. Despite being 'tailor-made' in this way the burrow is not a permanent

LEFT **Rarely seen by day, the aardvark is a solitary, secretive beast that spends much of its time underground. At night it emerges to forage for ants and termites, breaking into their nests using its** **powerful claws and licking them up with its long, sticky tongue, like an anteater.**
PAGE 309 **A group of Cape hyraxes huddle together beneath a rocky outcrop on the African plains.**

home, and an aardvark will frequently move to a new area and dig itself another. The old burrows are often taken over by other tenants, from monitor lizards and owls to warthogs and porcupines.

Aardvarks are solitary, nocturnal animals, and each individual occupies its own burrow. A mother and her single offspring will share a nest, but not for long; by the time it is six months old the young aardvark will move out and dig a new burrow, although it does not go far away. They feed mainly on termites, but also on ants, other insects and some plant matter. Like many creatures that eat termites and ants they have elongated snouts to enable them to probe deep into the nests, and long, sticky extendible tongues which they use to scoop up insects from the galleries within. Aardvarks feed at night, digging into large termite mounds, and using their keen sense of smell to track down termites that are out foraging in the open. The animal's thick skin protects it against being bitten by termites and other insects.

Colonial climbers

Hyraxes are rat-like animals that grow to the size of rabbits. They have short, broad heads with rounded ears, short legs and slender feet. There are four toes on their forefeet and three on their hind feet, and in both cases the side toes are rather small. This suggests that their ancestors were running animals, but today they are well adapted for climbing, with sticky pads on each foot that provide an excellent grip as they clamber among the rocks and branches. They will use a variety of techniques to find their way up apparently sheer ascents - for example, a hyrax will climb up a crack in the rock by wedging its back against one side and pushing itself up with its feet, exactly as a climber does when ascending a chimney.

There are three types of hyrax: the tree hyraxes, rock hyraxes and bush hyraxes. Tree hyraxes live mainly in the tropical forests of Africa, although they occur as far south as the Cape. The western tree hyrax is one of the more primitive species; it forages among the branches for leaves and young shoots during the day and takes refuge in hollow trunks at night. It is more solitary than the other hyraxes and does not form true colonies. These tree hyraxes have special dorsal glands that produce particularly abundant secretions during the mating season. The site of the gland is marked by a tuft of long, contrastingly-

ABOVE A tree hyrax reaches out to nibble a particularly tempting leaf. Although they have long incisor teeth, hyraxes rarely use them when feeding, preferring to slice off the foliage with their serrated molar teeth. Hyraxes are expert climbers; they have rubbery, adhesive pads on their feet that become moistened with sweat when they are active, giving an excellent grip on bare branches and rocks.

coloured hairs, which stiffen when the animal is excited. Both rock and bush hyraxes have similar glands, but they are less developed and not so obvious.

Tree hyraxes are not restricted to life in the trees. Some species, such as the southern tree hyrax, frequently live in rocky cavities formed in the *kopjes* (the Afrikaans word for hillock) - rock outcrops that stand 30-40m above the African plains. These mounds are often densely vegetated and form particularly important habitats for the other kinds of hyraxes.

ABOVE **A hawk's-eye view of a tree hyrax, showing the distinctive scent gland on its back, marked by a tuft of contrasting hair. Hyraxes frequently fall victim to large birds of prey, and the Verreaux's eagle feeds on little else. They are also preyed on by lions, leopards, hyenas and jackals, but prosper in areas where their habitat is undisturbed.**

Rock hyraxes, or dassies, which occur throughout much of central and southern Africa and parts of the Middle East, tend to eat fewer leaves than their tree-dwelling relatives, feeding mainly on grass. Such fibrous material is hard to digest, and like many of the ungulates hyraxes have evolved a system making use of micro-organisms which live in their stomachs and break down the tough cellulose in the plant cells. They have a curious way of eating: although they have long, prominent incisor teeth they use their cheek teeth to bite off leaves and grass, a method that involves turning their heads on one side. The front incisors are used for defence, and a hyrax can inflict quite deep wounds if cornered.

These animals are gregarious and form large colonies. One reason for this is that a hyrax cannot regulate its body temperature very effectively, and when the external temperature drops they have to huddle together to keep warm. The whole colony tends to urinate in the same place, depositing calcium compounds that crystallize on the rocks to form white 'hyraceum' deposits; these were once highly valued as medicine by African tribes and European settlers.

Considering their somewhat primitive make-up, hyraxes are a remarkably successful group of animals, with an ability to exploit a wide range of habitats. They fall victim to many predators such as leopards and eagles, but despite both this and a relatively low birth rate (two to three offspring at a time), their populations stay roughly constant. The tree hyraxes, however, are coming under threat: by erosion of their habitat as the forests are felled, and, particularly in the case of the eastern tree hyrax, by hunting for their fur.

Sirenia

The sirenians are the most remarkable of the sub-ungulates, for they have abandoned the way of life followed by their land- dwelling ancestors and taken to the water. In the process they have lost their hind limbs - although traces of the pelvic girdle remain - and have developed a streamlined, torpedo-like body shape very like that of a seal.

Unlike seals, however, sirenians feed on plants, grazing seagrasses and waterweed like submarine cattle (they are also known as sea cows). This diet of tough, gritty foliage, is very hard on their chewing teeth, and manatees continually renew them by shedding old ones and growing replacements. The new teeth form at the back of the manatee's mouth and push the whole row forward along the jawbone at the rate of about 1mm a month; by the time they reach the front of the row the teeth are worn down and fall out. Their relatives the elephants benefit from a similar system, and this is one of the clues to their common ancestry. The dugong eats softer plants, and its small molar teeth are not adapted in the same way - but adult males have two protruding incisors in their upper jaws, reminiscent of elephant tusks.

Manatees live in fresh or brackish, estuarine waters in tropical Africa and America. They are peaceful, tolerant animals, living in family groups made up of parents and offspring of different ages. There are three species, and of these the West Indian manatee is probably the most well understood owing to work carried out in the Everglades National Park in Florida. It is found in the lagoons, rivers and waterways of Florida, along the coasts of Caribbean islands and in

HYRAXES CLASSIFICATION

The 11 species of hyraxes make up the order Hyracoidea. They are divided into three genera: the tree hyraxes, rock hyraxes and bush hyraxes.

There are three species of tree hyraxes: the eastern tree hyrax *Dendrohyrax validus* of east Africa, the western tree hyrax *D. dorsalis* of west and central Africa, and the southern tree hyrax *D. arboreus* of south-east and east Africa.

The rock hyraxes are more numerous; there are five species distributed from south-west Africa to the eastern Mediterranean: the Abyssinian hyrax *Procavia habessinica*, Cape hyrax *P. capensis*, western hyrax *P. ruficeps*, Kaokoveld hyrax *P. welwitschii*, and Johnston's hyrax *P. johnstoni*.

Bush hyraxes are restricted to Africa, and found from the south-west to the north-east. There are three species: the Ahaggar hyrax *Heterohyrax antinae*, Bruce's yellow-spotted hyrax *H. brucei*, and the Matadi hyrax *H. chapini*.

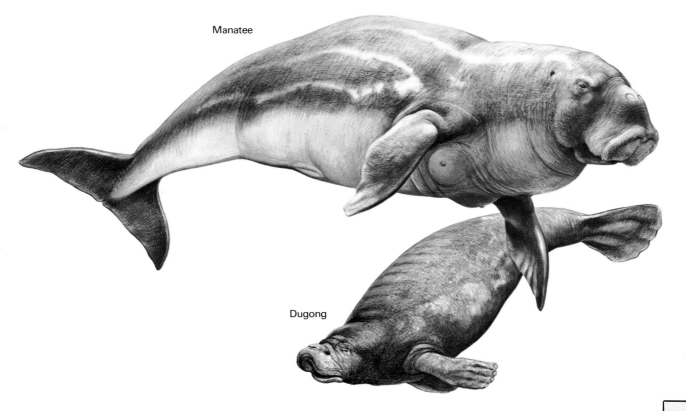

Manatee

Dugong

ABOVE Gleaming in the blue light filtering through the shallows, a shoal of fish swim round the blunt shape of a dugong as it drifts lazily over the sea bed. Dugongs live on the marine flowering plants known as seagrasses, grazing in the shallow coastal waters of the Pacific and Indian Oceans like underwater sheep or cattle, and digging out the thick, fleshy roots with their broad snouts.

SIRENIA CLASSIFICATION

Despite their seal-like appearance the sea cows of the order Sirenia are relatives of the hyraxes and elephants. They are divided into two families: the manatees and the dugong. There are three species of manatee, all found in rivers, estuaries and shallow coastal waters: the West Indian manatee *Trichechus manatus*, Amazonian manatee *T. inunguis* and West African manatee *T. senegalensis*. The dugong *Dugong dugon* is a marine species found in coastal shallows in the western Pacific and Indian Oceans. A giant sirenian, Steller's sea cow, formerly lived around two islands near eastern Siberia, but was hunted to extinction in the 18th century.

the clear, shallow coastal waters and river estuaries of north-eastern South America. The West African manatee has a similar habitat, and both species have downward-pointing muzzles adapted for feeding on the roots and foliage of plants growing on the sea bottom or the river bed. The Amazonian manatee is slightly different, as it is restricted to the fresh waters of the Amazon and its tributaries. It feeds mainly on the surface, browsing on the floating foliage of plants such as water lilies, and so its muzzle does not have the same pronounced downward angle as its relatives.

Although they are air-breathing mammals, manatees are completely dependent on their aquatic environment. Like whales they will die if they are stranded on dry land, but they can usually escape by heaving themselves back into the water using their mobile front limbs. They are good underwater swimmers, although they lack the acrobatic grace of the seals which need to hunt for their food. Manatees will remain underwater for periods of up to a quarter of an hour, feeding on submerged plants, before surfacing for two minutes or so to breathe.

The manatee has a very long intestine, designed to break down tough plants with the aid of cellulose-digesting bacteria living in the gut. So equipped, it is capable of consuming 50kg of vegetation every day.

ABOVE A family group of manatees bask in the clear waters of a lagoon in the Florida Everglades. Both manatees and dugongs have lost their hind limbs in the course of evolution, and acquired strong flipper-like tails.

BELOW The mermaids and sirens of legend may have been inspired by the curiously human attitude of the female manatee as she supports her young in the water. Manatees are very slow breeders, raising one calf every two years.

Such an appetite makes the manatee a rather useful animal, as far as water authorities are concerned. Introducing a group of manatees is one of the most efficient ways of clearing a lake or river that has become choked with water weed. The animal's value has been recognized at international level, and some countries have imported specimens into their own waters to help keep down excess vegetation. In spite of this all three species are in some danger, for they are widely hunted for their meat and have few defences.

The vulnerable dugong

The dugong is superficially similar to the manatee, but smaller. Mature adults may reach 4m in length and 900kg in weight, whereas a manatee can grow to 4.6m and weigh up to 1600kg. Unlike the manatee it lives entirely at sea, inhabiting the coastal waters of east Africa, the Red Sea, southern India, south-east Asia and northern Australia. Like the manatee it is a vegetarian, but the sea grasses that it eats are less abrasive than freshwater plants and it has no need for replaceable teeth. Its molars are small and peg-like, and it actually chews its food using horny plates on its upper and lower palate. Its tail is also different: whereas a manatee has a rounded flap, a dugong has a broad triangular tail rather like a dolphin's.

315

Dugongs live in family groups and browse in the shallows at depths of 2-3m. They generally feed during the night over an extensive area, retreating to deeper, more sheltered waters during the day and occasionally descending to 10m or more. A dugong gathers seagrasses by grasping strands in its mouth, ripping them from the bottom and then freeing them of sand and debris with its flippers before starting to chew. It is especially fond of the plant roots.

A relative of the dugong, Steller's sea cow, once lived around two islands in the Bering Sea, feeding on the kelp beds offshore. It was a giant sirenian, growing to three times the size of the dugong. The animal was unknown to science until a Russian sea expedition put ashore on one of the islands in 1741. Once discovered, it was hunted relentlessly for its meat and its hide. By 1768 the whole population had completely vanished from the seas.

LEFT A West Indian manatee surfaces for air and a brief look round before sinking to the bottom to gather more food. Manatees can be very useful in inland waterways, clearing the vegetation from choked channels and saving local water authorities the considerable expense of scouring them out mechanically.
BELOW The map shows the world distribution of the sirenians, hyraxes and aardvarks.

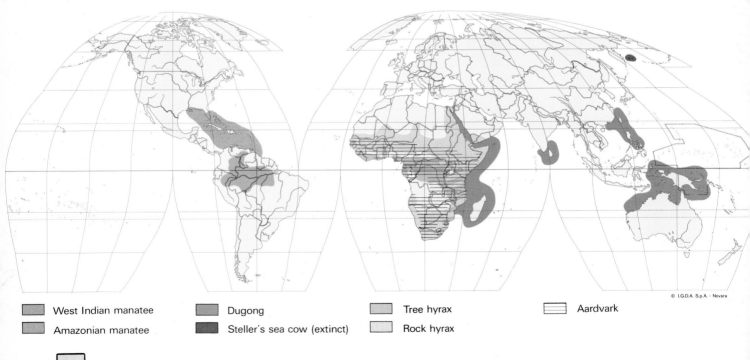

© I.G.D.A. S.p.A. - Novara

West Indian manatee	Dugong	Tree hyrax
Amazonian manatee	Steller's sea cow (extinct)	Rock hyrax
		Aardvark

THE GENTLE GIANTS

Largest of the land mammals,
but remarkably gentle and sensitive,
the elephant is one of the most spectacular
members of the animal kingdom

Elephants have always fascinated us with their great size, power and grace. The Roman armies took them into battle to overawe their enemies, and Indian princes used them as symbols of power and prestige. Trained Asian elephants have been employed as draught animals for centuries, and in south-east Asia the elephant was long the mainstay of the timber trade. In Africa there is no tradition of elephant domestication, and the animal has always been regarded as a source of meat and ivory. Unfortunately the inflated value of elephant ivory has encouraged illegal hunting on a massive scale, and for this and other reasons - notably the destruction of their habitats - both species are now under threat.

It is hard to visualize the common ancestor that produced the elephants, sea cows and hyraxes. The differences between the three families were less pronounced some 40 million years ago, when large hyraxes which resembled tapirs and stood about 1.2 metres tall, may have browsed alongside equally tapir-like forerunners of the modern elephant. During the ensuing millennia the elephants grew larger and more specialized, evolving into a variety of forms that reached a peak of diversity in the Pleistocene period, about two million years ago. These animals spread from Africa to every continent except Australia and Antarctica. By this time they had acquired most of the modern elephant's characteristics: a mobile trunk, long tusks, disc-like feet and, of course, enormous size. Biggest of all was the imperial mammoth, whose remains have been found in North America. After the Pleistocene most species became extinct.

A mobile nose

The elephant's most distinctive feature is its trunk. This is essentially an extension of the animal's top lip and nose. The elephant has an excellent sense of smell which plays a major part in detecting danger and in social encounters. But it is much more than a mobile smelling organ. It is equipped with strong muscles throughout its length, and has a sensitive tip that can be manipulated rather like a hand, enabling the elephant to feel, smell and grasp leaves, twigs and bark, tear them off and carry them to its mouth. The trunk can also be used to suck up water for drinking or bathing, to produce a variety of noises, as a snorkel when bathing, and to spray water, dust or sand over the elephant's body, not only to keep it cool, but to free it of parasites.

PAGE 317 **Dwarfed by the bulk of its mother, a new-born African elephant reaches up between her forelegs to suckle.**
LEFT **A majestic, high-crowned Asian elephant keeps watch as her calf plays in the muddy water of a river. The massive** head of an elephant may account for **20 per cent of its total weight.**
BELOW **An elephant's trunk has many uses. Here an African elephant gives her calf a lift up a shallow cliff, and (right) takes a drink while another female keeps guard.**

ABOVE A wild Indian elephant emerges into a clearing to drink before slipping back among the trees. Asian elephants are forest creatures, while their African cousins live on grassy plains.

LEFT Despite its rough appearance an elephant's skin is very sensitive, and needs to be washed and bathed in dust or mud to keep it free of parasites. It uses its trunk to spray itself with dry earth.

The trunk is essential to the elephant, for it has a short, comparatively rigid neck and cannot reach down to take food with its mouth like other large grazing or browsing animals. The short neck is necessary because its head is so heavy - it may account for a quarter of the elephant's total body weight - and it is probable that the trunk evolved as an alternative to the long neck possessed by animals such as the horse.

Tusks are used mainly for feeding, for example, prising off bark from trees, but also for digging out roots, displaying to other elephants, and as a weapon against predators or between bulls in the mating season. Tusks first appear when an elephant is about two years old and they are permanent, growing throughout the animal's life. A bull of 60 years or more may have a pair of tusks weighing 130kg each and stretching 3.5m in length. Cows have smaller tusks, or, in the case of some Asian animals, none at all.

Bulk feeder

Elephants eat an enormous quantity of food (up to 150kg for adults) and spend up to 80 per cent of the day collecting and eating plant material of all kinds, including grass, roots, bamboo, tree bark, leaves and fruit. Altogether the average daily intake adds up to over 50kg, and some animals have been known to eat several hundred kilograms in 24 hours. Water consumption too is great - some 60-90 litres a day. Elephants have to eat a lot, as they digest less than half of what they eat, excreting plant matter almost intact.

The elephant has only two types of teeth: incisors and molars. The single pair of upper incisors grow into the tusks. The four molars - two in the lower jaw and two in the upper jaw - are large teeth with broad, deeply ridged top surfaces. However, only one tooth on each side, above and below, is used to grind its food. As they are worn down they are continuously replaced by the tooth behind which moves forward to push out the worn stump; this occurs about five times during the elephant's life.

Coping with the heat

Because elephants are so large they have difficulty getting rid of excess heat. Small animals tend to lose heat easily, since they have a large surface area in relation to their body mass, and this acts as a very efficient radiator. For an elephant the ratio is reversed: it may weigh five times as much as, say, a camel, but have only twice the skin area. As a result the internal heat tends to build up faster than it can be radiated.

In a cold climate this would be an advantage, but in tropical areas it is a problem. The elephants solve it by immersing themselves in water at frequent intervals, and squirting water over their own and one another's backs. They also use their ears as radiators. Being thin flaps, the ears have a large surface area. They are also well-supplied with blood vessels: by flapping its ears the elephant can cool the blood running through them which then cools the rest of its body. It is significant that African savannah elephants living on the open, sun-baked plains have the largest ears of all; Asian elephants live in shady forested country, and their ears are much smaller.

An elephant's feet are remarkable. In skeletal terms it walks on its toes, like a deer, but the bones of each foot are embedded in a big wedge-shaped pad of fatty tissue so that, in effect, its feet are supported by wedge

ABOVE A young Asian elephant takes a shower. The trunk is a muscular extension of the upper lip and nose, with a delicate, mobile tip that can be used like a hand.
PAGES 322-323 A group of African elephants slake their thirst at a waterhole.

Elephants need a lot of water; a single animal may drink over 80 litres a day, sucking the water into its trunk and squirting it into its mouth. During times of drought they will use their trunks and tusks to dig into dried up riverbeds to find water.

African elephants live south of the Sahara; Asian elephants keep to forests in India, China and South-east Asia.

soles. The pads have broad circular bases that spread the weight of the elephant over a large area. As a result it leaves very shallow tracks, and can wade into lakes and rivers up to its belly without sinking into mud. Elephants can be extraordinarily silent and agile, and will often stretch out on the ground and roll around with much more grace than many smaller mammals. They rarely move fast, preferring a dignified, ambling gait of 4-6km per hour, making them comfortable and stable to ride. But a fleeing or charging elephant can reach 40km per hour.

A range of signals

Elephants communicate by sound, smell, touch and gesture. Although their sight is not poor it is less important to the social life of the elephant than the other senses. Sound signals are particularly significant, and include trumpeting, blowing, puffing and rumbling noises. They also have a very keen sense of smell, and an elephant will often raise its trunk in the air to pick up a scent carried by the breeze. Their sense of touch is probably second only to that of the primates, for the end of an elephant's trunk is equipped with sensory hairs that allow it to detect the precise nature of the objects it investigates and picks up.

ELEPHANTS CLASSIFICATION

Elephants belong to the order Proboscidea. There are two species: the larger is the African elephant *Loxodonta africana*, which occurs in savannah grassland and forests throughout much of Africa south of the Sahara. The elephants found in these two habitats are generally regarded as two subspecies: the savannah elephant *L. a. africana* and the forest elephant *L. a. cyclotis*. The so-called Cape elephant *L. a. oxyotis* is regarded by some as a full subspecies. It is confined mainly to the Addo National Park in South Africa.

The Asian elephant *Elephas maximus* is found in India, south China and south-east Asia. There are four subspecies: the Indian elephant *E. m. bengalensis*, Ceylon elephant *E. m. maximus*, Malaysian elephant *E. m. hirsutus* and Sumatran elephant *E. m. sumatrana*.

The trunk is also used to communicate by gesture. An elephant will appease another by placing the end of its trunk between its partner's lips, probably as a ritual offer of food. If it wants to express submission it will place its trunk in its mouth or use it to pull down its ears - just as a nervous person will finger his ear lobes. When an elephant is aroused it will spread its ears wide and raise its trunk, but if it decides to charge it will roll its trunk against its chest and fold back its ears before rushing headlong at its enemy. In general such charges are meant to intimidate possible adversaries rather than hurt them.

Elephants generally fight head-to-head. First they face one another at a distance of about ten metres, then grasp each other's trunks, rear up on their hind legs and cross tusks, grappling until one submits. This grasping technique makes it hard for the combatants to damage one another, and ensures that the species does not wipe itself out by internal rivalry.

A strange frenzy

One peculiar condition seen in both Indian and African male elephants during the mating season is 'must', an Indian word meaning 'intoxicated'. In this state glands in the animal's cheek and forehead secrete a liquid with a penetrating, bitter smell that runs down the side of the animal's face. The period of must may last from one day to one month, during which time the bull becomes very aggressive; elephant drivers in India chain up animals in must to trees because they regard them as so dangerous. Musty males use the secretions of the glands to mark trees and bushes. In the wild, the animals also defecate and urinate more frequently and accompany herds of females. Must is probably similar to the rut of deer bucks when males are physiologically capable of mating and seek to defend females from other males. In captivity, must is not essential for breeding as many males mate before 15 years old - the age when must starts. Even in the wild, females will mate with males who are not in must.

The Asian elephant

Superficially similar to its African cousin, the Asian elephant can be easily identified by its high-domed head, smaller ears and convex back. Its body is also slightly smaller, growing up to 3m high at the shoulders and weighing up to 5000kg. The animal also has shorter tusks than the African species.

ABOVE **An African bull elephant embraces the tusks of his prospective mate. It is usually the largest bull among competing males which mates with the female.** BELOW AND RIGHT **The elephant's trunk plays an** important part in its courtship ritual. After chasing the female (below) the male caresses her head, trunk and tusks (right), then strokes her back gently until she indicates that she is ready to mate.

ABOVE Restrained by a stout chain, a domesticated Asian elephant scratches itself against a tree as it munches its way through a sheaf of bamboo. Providing enough food for a captive elephant can be quite a problem, for an adult will eat approximately 150kg of vegetation a day.
BELOW An elephant uses its trunk to communicate in sign language, showing threat and aggression (top), and successive stages of submission (below).

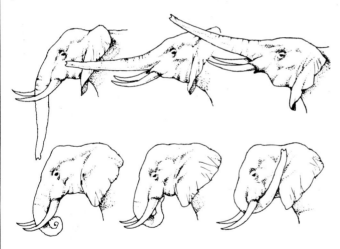

Asian elephants are distributed from Pakistan across south-east Asia to the islands of Indonesia. At one time they were even more widespread, but the demand for wild animals for domestication led to so much trapping that many elephant populations have disappeared. The erosion of their natural habitats and the activity of ivory poachers has worsened their position, and today there are thought to be no more than 40,000 Asian elephants left in the wild, scattered in relict forest patches. Thousands more are still kept in domestication as working animals.

A subspecies of the Asian elephant is found on the island of Sri Lanka; these Ceylon elephants are notable for the fact that only 10 per cent of males bear tusks, and the females never do. This makes them an unattractive target for poachers, and some 2500 Ceylon elephants are alive today, mostly in the protected parks of Rahuna, Yala, Gal Goya and Wilpattu. Survival seems to be assured for this subspecies. The same cannot be said for the Sumatran elephant and the few remaining specimens of the Malaysian subspecies found on the Malaccan peninsula, in Sumatra, and in Thailand.

Indian elephants live in the jungle. In hilly or mountainous areas they will climb up to over 2000m, showing great skill as mountaineers. They are forced to move with great care in these situations, especially during their tiring descents. Elephants are creatures of habit and always use the same tracks during their movements, creating a road network that may be used by other animals and man.

Life in the group

Elephants have a complex social system. Herds are usually family groups formed of up to 20 animals, led by an old female, but occasionally as many as 150 from different family groups may gather together. It is rare to find adult males (bulls) in a herd - they generally live alone or in 'bachelor groups' of two to four animals. The herd, therefore, comprises females (cows), their young and some juvenile animals who are probably the older offspring of the females. While the cows and young of a group tend to be related, other animals may join the herds.

Elephants usually breed when they are 11 years old, and pregnancy lasts 21 months. Baby elephants are about 90cm tall at birth and weigh 100-120kg; they reach 150-180cm in height by their fifth year (weighing almost one tonne). A ten-year-old female may reach a height of 180cm while a male exceeds 2m. Growth continues more slowly after the fifteenth year but does not stop entirely. Young elephants suckle with their mouth (not the trunk) from paired breasts between the mother's front legs, for three or four years. The maternal bond lasts a long time and it is quite normal to see a cow followed by young of different ages. Though young bulls generally leave their mother at the age of five or six, females up to ten years old may stay with their parents.

ABOVE Bathing is an important part of an elephant's routine, for it helps to keep it cool. Overheating is a constant hazard for a big mammal in a tropical climate, and African elephants often retreat to water or shade in the midday heat.

RIGHT Rival males size one another up (top), threaten each other with trunks raised (centre) and then attack (bottom). Elephants fight head to head, grappling only with their trunks and tusks, so that serious injuries are rarely inflicted on each other.

These daughters often act as helpers or 'aunts' in the rearing of younger siblings. During births, other females may gather round the newborn calf, blowing dust on it to dry it, and one may act as a 'midwife', removing the foetal membrane. Cows are able to bear young about once every four to five years, up to the age of 45. African elephants usually bear single, occasionally twin, calves; the Asian only a single calf.

Beasts of labour

Asian elephants have been used as working animals since ancient times. The first record of elephants as beasts of burden dates back 5,500 years to the Indus Valley. They are still important in parts of Asia, especially in logging operations where their strength is well used. There has always been a demand for elephants caught in the wild - rather than those bred

LEFT Led by an old matriarch, a family group of African elephants moves out of the shade to graze on the plain.
RIGHT A big bull Indian elephant, guided by his handler, begins its work.
BELOW RIGHT An African elephant raises its trunk to scratch the underside against a tree. Part of the bark has been stripped and eaten by these large animals which can cause much destruction to trees in the dry season.
BELOW Its tusks probing deep into the earth, an African elephant attempts to find some water during a drought.

in captivity - for elephants must be ten years old before training starts and they only really become useful at the age of 20.

In Asia, the 'khedda' is the classic system used to capture elephants. Lasting up to two months and employing some two thousand beaters, the khedda involves driving wild elephants towards a large capture pen. As soon as they are trapped the pen is closed. Those chosen to be trained are separated from their groups, and the rest are freed. They are then tamed and trained by skilled instructors.

Apart from being used as labouring animals, elephants still feature in ceremonial processions, religious tradition and popular festivity.

The African elephant

African elephants are slightly larger than their Asian relatives and have bigger, more rounded ears. The largest bull African elephant can reach three and a half metres in height at the shoulder and weigh seven and a half tonnes, though females are always smaller. The back of the African has a distinct hollow, and the end of the trunk has two lips rather than one as in the Asian. Both male and female African elephants have tusks.

At one time, the African elephant was found throughout the continent, except for desert areas.

European colonization in the 19th century, land reform, safaris and the ivory trade sealed the elephant's fate in many areas of west and southern Africa where the animal now survives only in national parks and game reserves. The most southerly colonies are found in the Addo National Park and Knsyna reserve in South Africa.

The situation is better in central Africa, where elephant numbers are thought to exceed 350,000, but in east Africa there has been a staggering decline in recent years. By 1987, the population had crashed from over 400,000 to less than 200,000 animals in just four years.

Population problems

When the continent was not as populated as it is now, elephants were able to roam over a vast area. Today, the growth of human settlements and farming has meant that elephants can no longer wander at will over their traditional routes. Their free movement is blocked by the boundaries of reserves and the fences of farmland. These restraints cause an unnatural buildup of a great many elephants in the parks, leading to the destruction of trees and shrubs.

A case in point is the Tsavo National Park in Kenya, where the elephants number some 20,000. Elephants used to visit this area only occasionally. But many newly-created water holes attracted large numbers of elephants and the local population increased alarmingly. During one very bad drought the elephants ate all the vegetation, leading not only to the starvation of many elephants but also to the death of half the park's number of rhinoceroses.

Tamed for war

The domestication of the African elephant was long shrouded in mystery. In the ancient world it was thought that only the Carthaginians possessed the art of taming the beasts, but it is more probable that they were using the smaller, now extinct, north African variety which were easier to tame than their southern relatives. They used the animals for their wars; in 218 BC the Carthaginian general, Hannibal, marched fifty African elephants over the Alps, though only eight survived the crossing. Today in the Gangalana Bodio forest station in Zaire, African elephants are trained for work to the same standards as the elephants in India and Burma.

UNDER THREAT

ELEPHANTS

Elephants have few enemies in the wild - the young are sometimes taken by large carnivores, but the adults have little to fear from other animals. Without doubt, their most dangerous foe is man.

Human predation on elephants has a long history. Hunting brought them to extinction in western Asia as far back as the 7th century BC, and over the last thousand years numbers in India have steadily declined. In Africa, the ivory trade began to strike elephant populations in the 17th century, and since then numbers have fallen drastically.

But it was not only hunting which threatened the animals. Indian elephants were prized as working animals, and many were taken from the wild into domestication. In both Africa and Asia human numbers gradually rose, increasing the demand for agricultural land, and submerging more and more space beneath roads and settlements. The elephants' natural habitats became reduced and fragmented, restricting their range and cutting off their migration routes. Stripped of their habitats, elephants soon perished.

Sadly, the pressures on elephants have intensified over recent decades. The value of ivory soared during the 1970s, bringing a wave of illegal hunting to Africa. Less than a million African elephants now remain, and, with killings proceeding at a rate of some 50,000-150,000 per year, the animal is nearing extinction with alarming speed. The toll is currently greatest in southern and east Africa. By 1987 east African elephants had halved their number in only four years, from over 400,000 to less than 200,000.

Asian elephants are already scarce in the wild, and they too are suffering from high poaching levels. There are believed to be no more than 40,000 animals left, scattered over Indonesia, south-east Asia and the Indian sub-continent.

BORN
TO RUN

Grazing the plains of Africa and Asia,
the wild members of the horse family have
evolved keen senses, sleek bodies, and feet
perfectly adapted for running

The horse family, the equids, is made up of the horses, the zebras and the asses, and contains seven species in all. Horses and asses both have a long history of domestication, but a small number of wild individuals still exist untamed and little-changed from their ancestors of long ago. All equids are herbivores, with long heads and necks, and slender legs, but the feature which sets them apart from all other animals is the structure of their feet. Each leg is supported on a single toe equipped with a broad hoof, and the two central bones of the foot are fused into a single very strong 'cannon bone', allowing horses to gallop over rough terrain without risking a fracture.

These changes have gradually taken place over the last 50 million years in the development of the horse-like mammals. Fortunately, we have a good record of their development in a series of fossils from successive stages in their evolution. The remains of the horse's earliest recognizable ancestor have been found in rocks laid down in the Eocene epoch, about 50 million years ago. Known as *Hyracotherium*, it was little larger than a fox, and instead of single hooves it had four toes at the front and three at the back. It lived in the forests of North America, and it was in this continent that much of the horse's evolution seems to have taken place.

As time went on the forests became replaced by grasslands, and the primitive equids adapted to the changes. *Merychippus*, which lived about 25 million years ago, had longer legs for galloping across the plains, and teeth specialised for chewing grasses.

Gradually, the horses grew taller and heavier, and their necks and muzzles became longer to enable them to graze in comfort. Meanwhile, the central hoof became larger and the side toes began to disappear. By about two million years ago the horses as we know them had developed.

PAGE 331 Now extinct in its native Mongolia, Przewalski's horse still survives in captivity, BELOW The zebras are the most striking members of the horse family. The purpose of their stripes is still debated, but most zoologists believe they serve as a kind of uniform, attracting the zebras to each other and forming a bond between them.

ABOVE Galloping to safety across an African plain, two Hartmann's zebras display speed and agility evolved as a defence against predators. With no cover for miles, the only way these zebras can escape an attacker is to outrun it.

RIGHT The evolution of the horses, showing how the main development took place in North America until the Pleistocene epoch. The column on the right shows the strengthening and simplification of the limb bones.

The modern horse

As we have noted, most of the horse's development occurred in the North American forests and prairies. From time to time, offshoots of the horse family colonized Eurasia (by crossing a narrow strip of land that once stretched between Alaska and Siberia), and the modern horse, *Equus*, followed their path. All the other horse-like mammals died out, but *Equus* flourished in the new continent, spreading into grasslands throughout its length.

Its descendants moved on to colonize Africa, and these Asian and African forms developed into the zebras, asses and horses of today. In America, however, all horses died out approximately 8000 years ago, and were unknown to native Americans until they were reintroduced by European colonists in the sixteenth century.

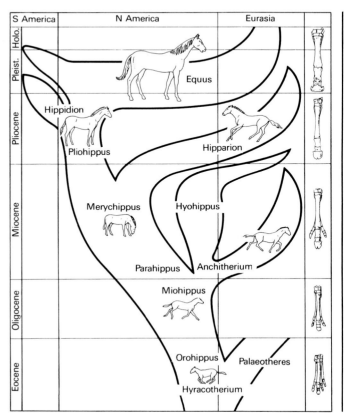

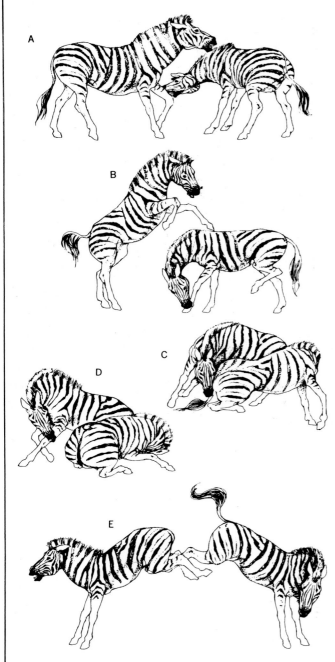

ABOVE **Zebra stallions will bite and kick as they fight over mares, but much of the action is ritualized and little real damage is done. The drawings show the various stages of a fight: (A) biting the neck and forelegs, (B) rearing up and kicking with the forelegs, (C-D) biting the tail and hind legs, and (E) kicking with the hind legs. Eventually one of the animals will submit or run away.**

Alert for danger

The seven species which make up the equid family are made up of three zebra, two ass and two horse species, one of which is the domestic horse. All members of the family have keen senses enabling them to keep alert for danger whilst grazing. They have an acute sense of smell, eyes set well back on the head providing a wide field of vision above the grass, and sensitive, mobile ears that can detect and locate the faintest sounds.

In some species, such as the wild horse and the plains zebra, it is common for individuals to take turns as look outs while the others graze. In due course there is a 'changing of the guard' and the watcher will get a chance to feed.

Horses need to spend more time grazing than many other ungulates. Their digestive systems are simpler than those of ruminants such as cattle or sheep, and over half the food they eat passes straight through. In consequence, a horse has to eat a good deal more than a cow to get the same supply of nutrients, and will often spend most of the day and night foraging for food.

Horses are able to survive on low-quality vegetation with limited food value. This means that they can live in habitats where grazing is poor and there is little competition for food from other animals. The last strongholds of the Asian wild asses and wild horses are arid semi-deserts, where the pasture is too poor for cattle and sheep.

Domestic horses, on the other hand, are generally fed on high-quality food containing grain, such as oats and barley. A certain amount of this is wasted, but it does supply the horse's needs more effectively. It also means that the horse does not have to spend most of its time grazing - a preoccupation which would be inconvenient in an animal kept to do a job of work.

Zebras

There are three species of zebras - the mountain zebra, the plains zebra, and Grevy's zebra - all of which are striped black-and-white and inhabit the grasslands of Africa.

The mountain zebra lives on the high grasslands of south-west Africa; it is slightly smaller and more lightly-built than the other zebras and has a different stripe pattern, particularly at the base of its tail. It occurs as two subspecies: the Cape mountain zebra

and Hartmann's zebra. Of these, the Cape mountain zebra is exceedingly rare. By 1913 the population had dwindled to 27 animals, and would have vanished altogether had the survivors not been placed under the strict protection of the Mountain Zebra National Park in the Cape Province of South Africa. Since then numbers have risen steadily.

The other subspecies, Hartmann's zebra, is more numerous, but has declined steadily from some 100,000 in 1920 to about 7000 animals living today, along the coast of south-west Africa.

Still plentiful

The plains zebra is by far the most numerous of all the zebras. It is the only wild member of the horse family which is still plentiful, though even this species is much reduced and fragmented in its range. Plains zebras are most common on the savannahs of east Africa, although their range extends down to the

RIGHT Slaughtered by the thousand for its beautiful hide with narrow-spaced stripes, Grevy's zebra has been brought to the edge of extinction by hunters. The largest of all the zebras, it also looks the most ass-like, with its large, broad ears and a long narrow head.
BELOW The map shows the world distribution of wild horses, asses and zebras.

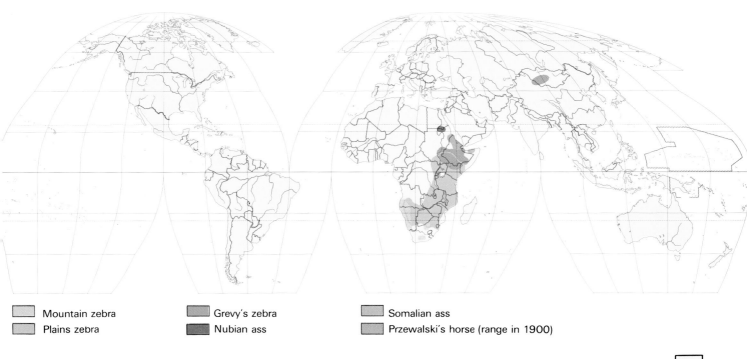

	Mountain zebra		Grevy's zebra		Somalian ass
	Plains zebra		Nubian ass		Przewalski's horse (range in 1900)

THE GRANT'S ZEBRA
— LIFE IN THE HERD —

Grant's zebra is a subspecies of the plains zebra, and ranges over the dry grasslands of east Africa from Zambia to Ethiopia. It is one of the best-documented species, thanks mainly to the work of Hans Klingel who made a close study of over 5500 specimens over a number of years. His researches have enabled us to build up a good picture of the social life of a zebra herd on the African plains.

In general, Grant's zebras live in family groups that consist of a male (stallion), a harem of females (mares) and their young foals. Young stallions remain with the group until they are four years old, when they leave to form bachelor herds. They are not chased off, but leave of their own accord, and the head stallion will often go in search of them if they wander away from the family group prematurely. Young mares will stay with the group for longer, and may even mate with the dominant stallion to produce zebra foals of their own.

By the age of five or six, a stallion is ready to leave his bachelor herd and collect a harem. Inevitably there is intense competition for mares in breeding condition, and even when the harem has gathered, the stallion has to be on constant guard against other stallions who try to lure mares away. He is helped somewhat by the fact that the mares do not all come into season at the same time, so he does not have to guard them all.

Ousting the head stallion

Occasionally an intruder will fight with the dominant stallion to win a mare, but more subtle and effective techniques can be employed. A well-timed raid, when the head stallion is busy elsewhere, will often suffice. In some cases the head stallion of a large herd may not be in full control, and another male may come to share his position. Eventually the younger animal will oust his senior altogether, often without a struggle. Old stallions invariably lose control of their harems at some stage, and go off to join bachelor herds.

This type of social organization means that young males who have left their mothers cannot occupy permanent

positions in the hierarchy until they have gathered their own harem. The dominant position in each herd is always occupied by a stallion, but despite this, he does not generally lead the herd as they travel between grazing sites. This role is usually carried out by a senior mare. The other mares recognize a strict subordinate hierarchy that is maintained at all times, and which is evident whenever the herd is on the move. Each mare travels with her foals, which are accorded honorary rank immediately below that of their mother and can share in her advantages. These may include being near the front of the queue at the waterhole, or gaining access to better grazing.

Imprinting identities

The group is very close-knit, and one result of this is that young foals will attach themselves to other mares if they get the chance. To prevent this, each mare tries to stay apart from the rest of the herd until her identity has been 'imprinted' in her foal's memory.

They will not allow other mares to approach their offspring during this critical period. As with all the horse family, the pregnancy is long - almost 12 months - and only one foal is born at a time.

LEFT A group of Grant's zebras at a shallow pool; one adult watches out for enemies while the others (including two foals) drink their fill.
TOP RIGHT A mare suckles her foal. Young zebras (and all horses) are well-developed at birth, and they are normally able to stand up on their feet within the hour.
CENTRE RIGHT A good scratch in the dust helps keep the skin free of parasites.
BOTTOM RIGHT Their teeth bared, two males wrestle neck-to-neck. A show of strength alone may be enough to settle such a contest, but zebras will also kick and bite to establish which is the dominant animal.

Grevy's zebra

Cape mountain zebra

Hartmann's zebra

Grant's zebra

Chapman's zebra

Quagga (extinct)

ABOVE **A Cape mountain zebra and her foal keep a look out for danger in the Mountain Zebra National Park of the Cape Province, South Africa. All members of the horse family have excellent vision and hearing; their eyes are set well back enabling them to keep watch while grazing, and by moving their ears to focus on a sound they can locate the source precisely.**

RIGHT **Every individual zebra has its own stripe pattern, but all the patterns tend to follow a basic scheme that differs according to the subspecies. Plains zebras (Grant's and Chapman's) have longer horizontal stripes than the mountain zebras (Cape mountain and Hartmann's). Grevy's zebra has very narrow, close-set, mainly vertical stripes.**

Cape. Two distinct subspecies exist today - Grant's and Chapman's zebras - but their colours tend to blend into one another across the continent. The more northerly Grant's zebra has sharp, distinct black-and-white stripes, while on the southerly Chapman's zebra the stripe pattern becomes blurred, with yellowish-brown in the pale stripes.

An extinct southern form of the plains zebra, known as the quagga, had distinct stripes only around the head and shoulders, while the rest of its body was a uniform brown. The quagga was wiped out in the 1880s - an early victim of the hunting and land development that threatens all African wildlife today.

Both mountain and plains zebras live in permanent groups, each consisting of a harem of females led by one male. Normally the group will forage within an area of 80-350 square kilometres, depending on the quality of the grazing. But in areas where the food supply dwindles in the dry season (as in the Serengeti), the harems will gather en masse and migrate together to greener pastures.

Grevy's zebra

Grevy's zebra is the largest of the zebras and different in many ways from the other species. A big specimen may weigh over 400kg, compared with 235kg for a plains zebra, and it has a distinctive coat pattern, with narrow, closely-spaced stripes. Unfortunately the hide has a high commercial value, and hunting has brought the species very close to extinction.

The mountain and plains zebras are similar to wild horses, but, in spite of its larger size, Grevy's zebra more closely resembles a wild ass. It has a long narrow head and big ears, and it brays like a donkey. Moreover, its behaviour is quite unlike that of other zebras and horses, and much more like that of the wild asses of Africa and Asia. The males tend to live alone within individual territories of up to 10 square kilometres, and they mate with female zebras that enter their territory. There are no harems, and associations between adults are normally temporary. Males without territories will often form bachelor groups, and females with young will band together, but they do not live in permanent herds like horses or other zebras.

The males mark their territories with large dung piles, replenishing each in turn; the resulting mounds

ABOVE An oryx shares a waterhole in southern Africa with a group of Chapman's zebras - one of the subspecies of the plains zebra.

BELOW Ritual displays of status are important in zebra society. Here a male (right) asserts its dominance over another in the group by raising and stretching its head. When about to fight for a female, males squeal to warn competitors.

Equids are widely scattered over east Africa, the Near East and across to Mongolia.

may be several square metres across and up to half a metre high. For much of the year, a territorial animal will not prevent other males entering his patch, provided they pay him due respect and make the appropriate gestures of submission. During the mating season, however, the resident male becomes less accommodating, and if a female on heat is present, he will actively defend the territory by seeing off any rivals. Having chased away the competition, he will attempt to guide the female to the centre of his territory and mate with her.

No hierarchy

The advantage of this type of social system is that each breeding male is in control of its own patch, and the males do not have to fight to achieve dominance over a number of females in a large area. Assuming there are enough females to go round, then each male will get his chance to mate.

One result of this territorial behaviour is that there is no hierarchy among Grevy's zebras as there is among animals that live in social groups. There is also little of the group responsibility shown by other species. Plains zebras, for example, tend to stay together while grazing, and some individuals will act as sentinels while others are eating; the males will also round up stray members of the harem and search for any that

have gone missing. Among Grevy's zebras, each animal looks out for itself and the only stable relationship is between a female and her foal.

This territorial system can be upset by changes in the climate. If there is a dry spell, the females and bachelor males will migrate to better pastures while the mature males stay put, guarding their territories. In conditions of prolonged drought, many mature males will travel a long way each day to eat and drink, then return to their own territories. Meanwhile the females may come into season without them - and the bachelor males will seize their chance to mate instead .

Why do zebras have stripes?

The precise purpose of the zebra's stripes is still unknown. Many brightly-coloured mammals such as tigers and jaguars appear to blend into the background when they are in their natural environment, but zebras live on the open plains where their stripes have no value as camouflage. Some zoologists have speculated that the stripes may dazzle potential predators, but this is not borne out by observation. A lion never shows any signs of confusion when it attacks a zebra, as one would expect if it was suffering from visual disorientation.

Since the colour scheme of the zebra seems to have little effect on its enemies, it may be intended to

EQUIDS
CLASSIFICATION

The Equidae are the only family of odd-toed ungulates with single hooves. The seven species fall into three distinct types: the zebras, asses and horses, but anatomically they are very similar and they are all classified in the same genus.

There are three species of zebra. The commonest is the plains zebra *E. burchelli* of east and southern Africa, which has two subspecies: Grant's zebra *E. b. granti* and Chapman's zebra *E. b. chapmani*. The mountain zebra *E. zebra* is found in the mountain grasslands of south-west Africa. There are two subspecies: the Cape mountain zebra *E. z. zebra* and Hartmann's zebra *E. z. hartmannae*. The rarest of the three species is Grevy's zebra *E. grevyi*, of east Africa which has a distinctive narrow-striped coat.

There are two species of ass. The African ass *E. africanus* of east Africa has three subspecies, and is the ancestor of the donkey. The Asiatic ass *E. hemionus* of south-west Asia, north India and Tibet has four subspecies. All wild asses are now considered to be endangered.

The domestic horse *Equus caballus* is found all over the world. Despite appearances all the various breeds, from the Shetland pony to heavy draught horses, belong to the same species. Feral horses (wild populations of the domestic horse) tend to be stockier in build. The wild horse *E. przewalskii* has only one surviving subspecies, Przewalski's horse *E. p. przewalskii* originally found on the plains of Mongolia but now existing only in captivity.

impress its friends instead. It has been suggested that zebras are strongly attracted to each other because they instinctively seek out the familiar striped pattern. Interestingly, the difference between the stripe patterns of the zebra species is greatest on their rump - zebras follow each other and so this is the part of their neighbour that they see most. Perhaps, then, the stripes are an aid to recognition, and help keep the herd together.

Other suggestions include the possibility that stripes help to regulate the body temperature, and there is even one theory that they serve to repel harmful flies.

African asses

The wild asses number two species - the African and the Asian asses - both of which have been brought to the edge of extinction.

The African ass was formerly abundant in the rocky deserts of north Africa, but it has now been reduced to a few scattered populations. It has three subspecies: the North African, the Nubian and the Somalian. Today the North African subspecies consists of a small number of animals that have escaped from domesticity and returned to the wild, finding food and water in the oases of the Sahara. The Nubian subspecies has dwindled to a few hundred individuals living within a restricted area of the eastern Sudan, and a mere sprinkling of Somalian asses now survive in Danakil and Somalia.

African asses are the smallest of the horse family, and weigh 200-300kg. They have narrow hooves, long ears and short, bristly manes. The Somalian ass is light grey with pinkish overtones, a brownish-black dorsal stripe and dark bands on its legs. The Nubian ass also has a grey coat, but with yellowish overtones. Its dark

ABOVE RIGHT Two Somalian asses show off their zebra-striped legs as they pick at the thin pasture. African asses - which include the Somalian subspecies - are now extremely rare in the wild, and their future might come to depend on the reintroduction of captive specimens into their natural habitat.
RIGHT The dark stripe running along the back of a Nubian ass forms a cross at the animal's shoulders. This distinctive marking has been inherited by the Nubian ass's direct descendant - the domestic ass, or donkey, which was first bred by the Egyptians some 6000 years ago.
PAGES 342 AND 343 A herd of Grant's zebras, a dazzling spectacle, gather to drink at a densely overgrown waterhole.

LEFT AND CENTRE Asian wild asses such as the onager can survive in the most arid, unpromising terrain. They often have to, for they have been driven out of more fertile areas by farmers.

However, a captive onager may enjoy richer pastures. BELOW LEFT A male onager curls back his top lip as he picks up the smell of a female (left), and bares his teeth in a threatening gesture (right).

dorsal stripe is intersected by another at right angles, forming a cross over the shoulders. This is also a feature of the North African ass - and it has been inherited by its domestic descendant, the donkey. According to religious tradition, this cross is the symbol given to the species when Christ rode on the back of an ass into Jerusalem.

The Egyptians seem to have domesticated the ass in about 4000 BC. It was an ideal working animal for farmers in the parched Mediterranean lands, owing to its sturdy nature and undemanding appetite. It was probably introduced to Europe by the Etruscans between 2000 and 1000 BC, and has flourished wherever there are peasant farmers who are unable to meet the expense of buying and keeping a horse.

Equal importance

In the wild, the social behaviour of the African ass is very similar to that of Grevy's zebra. There is no real herd structure and no hierarchy, and all individuals are equal in importance. In areas where they still survive, they live in small groups made up of 10-15 individuals. The males are solitary and only a certain number are territorial, occupying areas up to 15 square kilometres - half as much again as the territories of Grevy's zebra. The non-territorial animals tend to move around within favoured, familiar tracts of land. Of necessity, they are frugal animals, for they have to survive on the few thorny shrubs and withered plants that their arid, semi-desert environment can offer.

Although the African wild ass is an endangered species, it may still be saved by reintroductions to the wild from breeding populations that have been maintained in captivity. There are two major breeding centres: at Hellabrunn (part of Munich Zoo) and at the Catskill Game Farm in the United States. The German centre keeps the Nubian subspecies while the American centre has the Somalian, and the breeding herds are carefully controlled to ensure that the strains remain pure.

RIGHT **Three views of Przewalski's horse. Now extinct in the wild, Przewalski's horse survives in a few zoos and wildlife parks scattered throughout the world. It is** the last of the true wild horses that once roamed the central Asian plains, and can be easily distinguished from the domestic horses by its upright, bristly mane.

Asian asses

Once very numerous, the various subspecies of the Asian wild ass have been reduced to the point where they are highly vulnerable to further loss of their habitat. Several subspecies have already disappeared, and those that remain will continue to fall in number unless they can be guaranteed freedom from being disturbed in their natural environment.

At the end of the eighteenth century the Asian ass had an extremely wide distribution, from European Russia in the north to Asia Minor, Syria, Iraq, Iran and northern Arabia in the south, and extending eastwards across Central Asia as far as India, Tibet and Mongolia. With such a large range it was inevitable that local populations should have become separated, even at a period when the species as a whole was numerous. These populations developed independently to suit local conditions, gradually evolving into the distinct subspecies.

It is hard to define the actual number of subspecies that existed in the past, because the ancient writers tended to use the same names for different animals, or, conversely, employed different names for the same animal. However, careful sifting of the evidence available suggests that seven subspecies were to be found on the arid deserts of Asia until fairly recently. Of these, four survive.

The Syrian wild ass is the rarest; originally it was found throughout Syria, northern Arabia and Iraq, but today its status is highly precarious, and it may already have died out in the wild. The onager is in rather better shape, although it too has dwindled alarmingly in numbers. At one time it was widespread from Kazakhstan to European Russia, but now it is restricted to northern Iran and a reserve in Turkmenistan. The remote parts of the Gobi Desert in Mongolia and northern China still harbour a subspecies known as the kulan, while the largest of the subspecies, the kiang, survives in quite large numbers on the high Tibetan plains at altitudes well above the tree line.

Speed and stamina

Asian wild asses are more horse-like than the African asses, though they are relatively small in size, weighing some 200-300kg. They may be brownish yellow, sandy yellow or light grey, and like all asses they have long ears and tasselled tails (only the true horses have long hair growing along the full length of the tail). Their physical capacity matches that of the horse; it has been calculated that an Asian wild ass can maintain a steady pace of 40-50km per hour with occasional spurts of 60-70km per hour. Their main enemies are the wolf packs that roam the Asian plains and mountains, and hunt their prey by running it

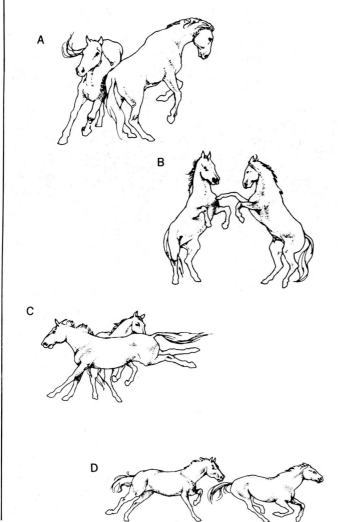

down in the open. In such circumstances, a good turn of speed and sufficient stamina are invaluable qualities.

The kiang is a particularly interesting subspecies because it has developed a number of adaptations to life in the mountains. It has a thick layer of fat beneath its skin to help it survive the bitter cold of a Himalayan winter, and its mouth and palate are specially hardened so that it can eat the toughest mountain plants. It is also larger than the other subspecies, and this is another feature that helps it survive in exposed conditions: larger animals are better able to conserve heat than their smaller relatives because their body mass is greater in proportion to their skin surface area. This means that less body heat is radiated to the surrounding air.

As a rule, male wild asses live alone and defend their own territories, but according to some observers the social life of the kiang resembles that of the plains zebra, in that dominant males gather harems of females and mate with them all. Each male may acquire up to 30 females, defending them against lower-ranking males that form bachelor herds. When the dominant male begins to weaken, another will challenge and may take his place. Like other members of the horse family, the Asian wild asses are gregarious animals, and they often mingle with herds of wild sheep and antelopes such as the saiga and chiru.

Wild horses

At the end of the nineteenth century wild horses were numerous on the steppes of Central Asia, and opinions differed concerning their origin. Some naturalists considered them to be the forerunners of our domestic horses, while others believed them to be no more than descendants of domestic animals that had returned to the wild. These horses displayed all the features of authentic wild animals, and were considered to be so by the Tartars and Cossacks. We now know that the Tartars and Cossacks were right. The wild horses were not domestic horses that had escaped and bred, but were descendants of the original wild animal from which all modern horses have developed. A hundred years ago they were to be seen roaming the grasslands in herds; today they have nearly all gone.

It seems that the wild horses all belong to one species. This species split into a number of subspecies that once inhabited the grasslands and steppes of

FAR LEFT Two domestic stallions fight for supremacy. (A) At first they strike one another with their flanks, (B) then they rear up at each other. (C) As the fight develops they kick and bite until (D) one breaks off and runs away.

ABOVE Elegant, powerful and fast, the thoroughbred is the ultimate expression of the horse-breeder's art. There are now some 200 breeds of the domestic horse, ranging from big, draught animals like the Shire to the small but hardy ponies.

Eurasia. Some of these forms died out in the wild during the early history of man, but their characteristics have been inherited by the modern domestic horse. Only three of the subspecies survived into the nineteenth century: the tarpan, the wood tarpan and Przewalski's horse.

The last wild horses

The tarpan lived on the steppes of southern Russia up to the nineteenth century, but the last remaining animals died in 1870 at Askanija Nova near the Crimea. The wood tarpan was recorded in wooded areas of eastern and central Europe during the Middle Ages, but it also disappeared in the nineteenth century. The last sighting was reported in the Zamosc region near Lublin in eastern Poland. Przewalski's horse fared better, surviving into the 20th century.

However, it was last seen in the wild in 1968, and it is almost certain that the population has been reduced to the 200 or so individuals that are now kept in zoos throughout the world.

These wild horses died out because of the disappearance of their habitat and their persecution by man. As the steppelands were developed, the most fertile areas were ploughed up, and the rest were overrun with domestic livestock. The farmers regarded the wild horses as pests, since they competed for grazing land with domestic horses, often succeeding in enticing away the females and seriously disturbing the otherwise peaceful herds. Inevitably they were hunted down and killed as pests. The captive Przewalski's horses now probably form the only living link with those wild herds.

Przewalski's horse

When it was discovered in 1879, Przewalski's horse lived on the grasslands and arid semi-deserts of north-eastern China, the Altai mountains and Mongolia. It is a stocky, short-legged animal with a dun-coloured coat, pale muzzle and belly, and dark legs, mane and tail. Its mane is bristly and erect, like that of an ass or a zebra, while that of a domestic horse falls to the side of its neck. Otherwise it is very similar to a domestic horse.

Tarpans also showed many similarities to domestic horses, and we know that they formed part of the original breeding stock from which these horses were derived. A few far-sighted breeders tried to save some of the tarpans before they died out, and the owner of Askanija Nova (today a nature reserve) created a special stud to breed the tarpan. Sadly, the project failed, and the wild herds died out, but their characteristics have not entirely disappeared. When they were still found, it was common practice to capture females (an easy task if the dominant male had been killed), domesticate them and use them for breeding. As a result, many domestic horses of Poland, the Ukraine and southern Russia shared, and still share, features reminiscent of the tarpan.

In the 1930s an attempt was made to 'reconstruct' the animal by selectively breeding some of these domestic horses to accentuate their wild characteristics. The experiment was carried out simultaneously in Poland and Germany and met with great success. A number of zoos and nature reserves now possess 'reconstructed' tarpans.

Living in clans

Studies of captive Przewalski's horses, and of domestic horses that have escaped, suggest that the wild horse's behaviour is very similar to that of the plains zebra. The horses live in 'clans' led by dominant males, and each clan has its own internal hierarchy. Membership of the clan is permanent, although the status of each member changes as the power of the dominant animals wanes and others take their place. Each clan has its own home range - the area that is regularly grazed - but this overlaps with the home ranges of other clans, and the males do not defend territories in the same way as the asses or Grevy's zebra. They reserve their aggression for other males who try to steal their females, and each male spends a lot of time running round the harem, keeping stragglers in line and warning off any potential male rivals.

Groups of horses will often gather in patterns such as the 'ring formation' when the animals stand in a circle with their heads facing inwards, and all swish their long tails at the same time. Another pattern is the 'chain formation' when they follow one another in single file, so closely that insects are brushed away by the tail of the animal in front.

The domestic horse

The horse has been domesticated in various stages throughout history, and in many different parts of the world. The nomads of central Asia were probably the first to ride horses, possibly as early as 2000 BC, and the Hittites (1700-1200 BC) introduced them to Mesopotamia. We know they were used in China during the Bronze Age Shang dynasty of 1600 BC to 1030 BC, because the remains of chariots and ritually-sacrificed horses have been excavated from royal tombs. The mobility and speed provided by the horse gave its owner a huge advantage over his enemies in war, and the Central Asian tribes were to exploit this in the series of conquests which established the Mongol Empire around 1200 AD.

It is likely that all domestic horses are descended from the same distant ancestors, which crossed into Eurasia from North America. These eventually split into a number of forms from which the variety of modern horses were derived. Generations of breeders gradually transformed the horses they domesticated.

There are now about 200 breeds of the domestic horse, but they fall into three main categories within the one species: workhorses, sports horses and ponies. The workhorses seem to have been bred from wild horses which lived on the tundra and from the tarpans of the steppes. The tundra horses were large, robust animals, adapted for life in cold northern latitudes, and their excavated remains show many similarities with big draught breeds such as the Shire and Percheron. The more high-spirited sports horses, such as the thoroughbreds, have their origins mainly in horses which spread from Asia into North Africa and Arabia, developing small teeth and tapering jaws. The many breeds of pony were derived from small, tough animals once found throughout northern Europe and northern Asia.

New World horses

Although the earliest ancestors of the modern horse originated in North America, they became extinct in prehistoric times, and all the 'wild' horses found in America today are derived from domestic horses. The first horses to appear in the New World were the seven animals Hernan Cortes brought with him when he landed at Veracruz in 1519. The descendants of those horses, and of innumerable others, were to give rise to the mustangs of North America.

TIMID FOREST DWELLERS

Shy, water-loving tapirs have kept their primitive shape for 20 million years, and despite resembling pigs with short trunks, they are related to rhinos and horses

TOP Camouflaged to blend in with the dappled light and shade of the forest floor, a young Malayan tapir is well-disguised during the first few months of life.
CENTRE The adult Malayan tapir is more dramatically coloured, but this, too, is a camouflage: the stark contrast between the black and white breaks up the tapir's outline as it moves through the trees. **BOTTOM Two male tapirs approach, sniffing each other suspiciously. PAGE 349 A group of Malayan tapirs enjoy a refreshing cool off in the water.**

Although the horses evolved dramatically over the millennia, their relatives the tapirs changed very little. The modern forms are much the same as *Protapirus*, a tapir that lived throughout Europe during the early Oligocene epoch about 35 million years ago. The basic reason for this is that tapirs never made the move out of the forests and onto the open grasslands. They kept their browsing habits and body shape while other ungulates had to adapt to a diet of grass and develop the capacity for sustained speed in order to escape predators.

Tapirs have certain physical characteristics that are common among animals living amid thick vegetation. These include agility, speed over short distances, and a sturdy, compact, streamlined body. With its narrow head and broad rump, a tapir is shaped like a wedge - the perfect design for an animal that escapes its enemies by dashing into thick undergrowth at high speed. Pigs are the same shape, for the same reason.

A trunk-like lip

Since tapirs still rely on the diet of leaves eaten by the earliest ungulates, their teeth have changed little, and are quite primitive compared to the complex chewing teeth of animals such as horses. Yet tapirs are not entirely unspecialized, for they have evolved one feature that makes them very efficient browsers - a short, mobile extension of the upper lip that performs much the same function as an elephant's trunk. It can be used to probe the tapir's surroundings, haul down branches and tear away the foliage, although all these functions are restricted by the length of the snout, which is no more than 17cm.

Although at first glance a tapir looks rather like a cross between a pig and an elephant, its affinities with horses become more apparent when it is seen in action. It has swift, agile movements, and a very horse-like way of snorting air out of its nostrils. It also leaps into action like a horse, cantering round and galloping into cover. It is probable that the early ancestors of the modern horses resembled tapirs both physically and in their behaviour, and the two types began to diverge only when the grasslands tempted the horse out of the forests and into the open.

One of the most interesting features of the tapir family is its geographical distribution. Three of the species live in South and Central America, but the fourth is found in South-east Asia, on the other side of

Three tapir species live in South and Central America; only the Malayan tapir is found in South-east Asia.

RIGHT **Protected from the cold by its thick coat, the mountain tapir of the northern Andes will often climb up to the edge of the permanent snow in search of succulent foliage. Like all tapirs it forages by night, moving from bush to bush and** never staying in one place for more than a few minutes. If it is alarmed it will sprint for the nearest cover and bury itself in the dense vegetation, or dive into water and stay submerged until the danger is past.

the world. It is possible that the Malayan species is a descendant of tapirs that colonized Asia when that continent and South America were joined together, and became isolated when the two landmasses drifted apart. The South American species flourished, since there was little competition for a large leaf-eating mammal in the South American forests. Asia, however, was well populated with animals occupying the same habitat (the rhinoceros and the elephant, for example) so the tapirs found it harder to compete. As a result only one Asian species has survived.

A woolly coat

Baird's tapir is the largest of the South American species, reaching 120cm at the shoulder and up to 300kg in weight. The Andean or mountain tapir is the smallest (weighing about 200kg) and most elegant species, with a slender neck and a downy coat that is thicker on the underside. This is probably an adaptation to life at high altitudes, since this tapir lives at heights of up to 4000m, which is close to the permanent snow line.

Despite its ability to withstand the cold, the mountain tapir is restricted to the equatorial area north of the Andean chain where it has access to the vegetation of tropical forests. The Brazilian tapir is the most widespread species, and for this reason it is also the least endangered. It can be found throughout the Amazon basin, rarely straying far from water. In size, it weighs about 250kg and measures about 100cm at the shoulder.

The Malayan tapir used to be common throughout Burma, Thailand, Malaya and Sumatra. Today it is very rare in the north of its range, as it is hunted for its meat and skin (the leather is highly prized, especially for horse bridles and whips). In Sumatra, Muslims consider it an 'impure', inedible animal like the pig, and so do not regard it as a source of easy meat. It is the largest of the tapirs, and a big specimen may weigh

as much as 375kg. It is also the most attractive, with a startling colour scheme consisting of a black head, shoulders, forelegs and hind legs, and a white back and flanks. Remarkably, considering its appearance and size, it was unknown to western science until the early 19th century, although it was well known to the Chinese, who had been including it in their dictionaries and natural histories for centuries.

In the tropical forest

Tapirs are animals of humid, tropical forests, where they feed on leaves, shoots, buds, fruit and tender young twigs in the undergrowth. They will also eat grasses and water plants. They are excellent swimmers and will often cross wide, swift-flowing rivers. Like other large animals in the tropics, they use water as a means of cooling down and freeing themselves of skin parasites; they will also take to the water if they are attacked by large predators, and are quite capable of staying submerged for several minutes at a time, walking on the bottom like hippopotamuses.

Since their main habitat is the forest, where visibility is limited, the senses of tapirs have developed accordingly. They have poor eyesight and can only spot moving objects, but their hearing is good and their sense of smell is acute. This is important in defence, giving them early warning of predators such as jaguars (in South America) or leopards and tigers (in Asia), but scent also plays a key role in communication. The most important scent marker is urine, which evaporates to form crystals of a startling whiteness. Faeces seem to be of little importance as scent signals because they are usually passed directly into water. In captivity, tapirs deposit all their droppings in the same place and do not kick them around.

Tapirs create pathways through the forest that nearly always start or end at watercourses. The paths often ascend steep slopes and follow river banks, and by repeated passage the tapir knocks the new growth off the surrounding vegetation to create green tunnels and galleries that vary in size according to the species. Those made by Baird's tapir are large enough to be used by other animals - and even people.

Although the South American species are still quite numerous, very little is known about their behaviour. They appear to be creatures of habit, and almost exclusively nocturnal - especially in areas where they are threatened by man. They are solitary animals, although they seem quite prepared to feed together on occasions. Each animal is dominant in its own territory. Intruders are warned off with snorts and cries, or are threatened with bared teeth - a threat posture that is reminiscent of the horses.

Noisy courtship

Mating is preceded by a complex and noisy courtship ritual that consists mainly of sound and scent signals: a series of squeals accompanied by repeated urination. In due course the partners position themselves nose to tail and circle round sniffing one another like dogs, and apparently trying to bite one another's hind legs. Meanwhile the male often tries to put his head under the female's belly. A similar form of behaviour can be noted among horses, especially during encounters between rivals. As in many other animal courtships, this may be a way of ritualizing their aggression.

Females come into season every eight weeks, and may give birth to young every 18 months or so. There are cases of tapirs producing no less than 10 young in 15 years, all born singly. Twins appear to be very unusual. All young tapirs bear characteristic flecked markings like those of new-born wild piglets and many young deer; these offer near-perfect camouflage in the dappled light of the forest. The markings begin to fade after two or three months, and at six months, when the young tapir is becoming independent, they have vanished altogether.

Tapirs become sexually mature at around three years old, and in captivity they may live for some 30 years. In the wild their life expectancy is probably much shorter, owing to disease and predation. Their principal natural enemies are the big cats (although

these are becoming as rare as the tapirs, if not rarer). Baird's tapir and the Brazilian tapir have evolved a defence against attack in the form of a short, bristly mane; a jaguar leaping on the tapir's back and attempting to deliver a fatal bite to the neck gets a mouthful of bristly hair, and this may give the victim a chance to brush off its attacker by rushing into the dense undergrowth.

The human threat

Inevitably, as is sadly so often the case, human greed is a far greater threat to the tapirs than any jaguar or tiger, and today all the species are endangered animals. The destruction of the forest for timber and agriculture is the main problem. Tree-felling in itself does not affect tapirs since it tends to promote rapid regrowth of bushes and shrubs, and an abundance of young shoots. Nevertheless, the disturbance caused by forestry developments, and the actual destruction of the habitat, are major threats to their survival. Tapirs can survive on the farmland that often takes the place of the forest, but only by raiding the farmer's crops - they will often cause considerable damage to cereals and maize as well as sugar cane and melon plantations, especially in Central and South America - and this encourages the farmers to regard them as pests, with predictable results.

TAPIRS CLASSIFICATION

The tapirs are odd-toed ungulates like the horses and rhinoceroses. There are four species, all classed in the same genus, and they make up the family Tapiridae.

Three species are found in South and Central America. The Brazilian tapir *Tapirus terrestris* is found near rivers in forests and on grassland from Venezuela south to northern Paraguay; Baird's tapir *T. bairdi* lives in similar country but has a more northerly distribution, from Mexico to Ecuador. The mountain tapir *T. pinchaque* lives in the mountain forests of the Andes of Ecuador, Peru and Colombia.

The fourth species is the Malayan tapir *T. indicus*, a native of the dense rain forests of Southeast Asia.

ARMOUR-CLAD SURVIVORS

Relics of another age, the tank-like rhinos are
well-armoured against any animal predators
but vulnerable to poaching for their horns

Sumatran rhinoceros

Indian rhinoceros

Black rhinoceros

White rhinoceros

Rhinoceroses are large, tough-skinned herbivores immediately recognizable by the prominent horn (or horns, depending on the species) on their snouts. The name 'rhinoceros' comes from two Greek words 'rhinos' (nose) and 'keras' (horn). Unlike the horns of cattle, sheep or antelopes, those of the rhinos have no bony core; they consist of a densely packed outer layer of tough keratin fibres mounted on a roughened area of the skull. Although their eyesight is poor, rhinos have very well developed senses of smell and hearing. Rhinos are a declining group of mammals. In prehistoric times they were numerous and varied, but today they are heading towards extinction - unfortunately helped by man.

The Asian rhinos

Three species of rhino live in Asia. The Indian or greater one-horned rhinoceros is the most westerly of the species. Once found along the length of the Ganges and Brahmaputra rivers, it is now largely confined to national parks such as the Chitwam in Nepal and the Kaziranga in Assam. Although some 1700 animals survive today - a vast improvement on the 40 or so animals that existed in 1910 - the Indian rhino is still regarded as endangered.

The Indian rhino is a good swimmer. It lives a largely solitary life, except when males and females meet briefly to breed or when a mother is rearing her young. Females occupy home ranges extending over nine to fifteen square kilometres; these areas overlap and are undefended, and the animal may wander even further afield in search of food and water. Males have larger home ranges, which they will occasionally defend. Neighbours rarely fight or confront each other. Conflict may arise when a strange adult male enters another's area, but a dominant male will

BELOW A young black rhino follows its mother across a grassy African plain. While calves of the black rhinos trail behind, those of the white and Indian rhinos tend to run in front of their mothers. Black rhinos are relatively small at birth and weigh about 40kg compared to 65kg for the white and Indian rhinos. PAGE 353 A pair of black rhinos standing in their scrubland habitat carry oxpeckers on their backs.

ABOVE The black rhino is the most widespread of rhino species but has suffered a drastic decline in numbers. Less than 9,000 black rhinos survive today and poaching continues to take its toll of populations.
BELOW The map shows the world distribution of rhinoceroses.

tolerate the presence of a weaker or non-breeding male in his home range.

Males and females deposit dung at selected points along their pathways to proclaim ownership of their right of way, and to mark out the boundaries of home ranges. In this manner, areas of common passage plus more private areas, usually used by only one individual, can be distinguished.

Indian rhino males become sexually mature at about seven to eight years old but usually do not mate until about ten years or more. Female Indian rhinos are able to calve at six to eight years old. Courtship is preceded by long, noisy chases and mock battles between the sexes. Newborn Indian rhinos, like the white rhinos of Africa, weigh 65kg - about four per cent of their mother's weight. Single young are born after a 16 month gestation and will remain with the mother until the birth of her next infant.

A remnant population

The Javan or lesser one-horned rhinoceros (once found in Sumatra, Java, Indochina, China, and in Assam up as far as the Ganges Delta) is now severely reduced in numbers. Only about 50 survive in the Udjong Kulon Reserve near Jakarta, with possibly a few hanging on in remote parts of Indochina, making it one of the most endangered of all mammal species.

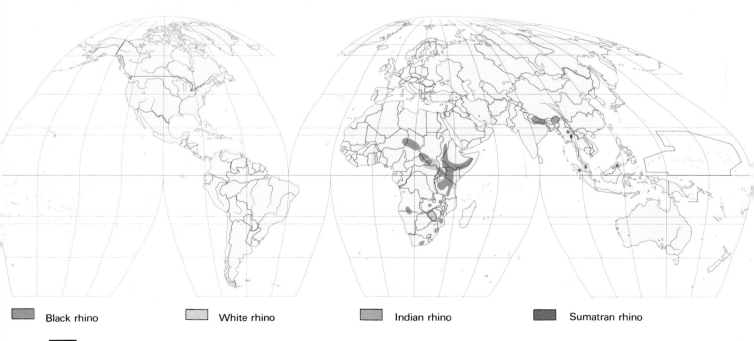

Black rhino   White rhino   Indian rhino   Sumatran rhino

Scattered populations of the Sumatran or Asian two-horned rhinoceros inhabit Borneo, Burma, Thailand, Sumatra and Malaysia today; formerly it ranged from Assam and Bengal to Vietnam and south to Borneo. It is found in several national parks such as the Taman Negara in Malaysia and the Kinabalu in Borneo. Probably no more than 150 animals exist today.

The skins of Indian and Javan rhinos are hairless. The larger Indian species may measure up to 1.9m at the shoulder and weigh up to two and a quarter tonnes. The Javan rhino is slightly smaller; it grows up to 1.7m high and weighs up to one and a half tonnes. The Sumatran rhino is still smaller, standing up to 1.4m and weighing up to 800kg. It is also distinguished by a sparse covering of long hair.

The African rhinos

Two species of rhino live in Africa: the black (or hooked- lipped) rhinoceros, and the white (or square-lipped) rhinoceros. Both species have two horns and virtually hairless skins and are found in more arid regions than their Asian relatives, though they still need water for mud baths and drinking. The white rhino is the giant of the family, measuring up to two metres high at the shoulders and weighing two and a half to three and a half tonnes - a bulk exceeded in land mammals only by the elephants. As with the Indian rhino, mature white rhino males are much larger than the females. The black rhino is about the same size as the Javan rhino - up to 1.6m high and weighing up to 1.3 tonnes.

Spotting the difference

Since white and black rhinos are actually grey in colour, the best way to tell them apart is by comparing their shapes. White rhinos have a prominent hump on the back of their necks which contains the ligament needed to support their huge head. They also have a

TOP **The immense bulk and single horn of the Indian rhino appear through the tangle of grass and bushes of its habitat.**
ABOVE **Two Indian rhinos enjoy a long bathe in the heat of the day. The** armour-plated appearance of the Indian rhino is due to the many folds and the bumpy surface of the skin.
BELOW **Two male rhinos meet nose-to-nose in order to investigate each other by scent.**

longer muzzle and broader mouth than the black rhino. Black rhinos have a lengthened upper lip which can grasp the branches of bushes and shrubs on which they feed.

Black rhinos

The black rhino is found throughout most of central and southern Africa. The greatest numbers are found in Tanzania and Kenya, mainly in the national parks, such as Serengeti, Ngorongoro, Masai-Mara, Amboseli and Tsavo. It is relatively abundant and widespread. But it was once much more numerous. In 1980 there were some 15,000 black rhino; today, poaching throughout its range, especially south of the Zambezi river, has seriously depleted many black rhino populations and there are now under 9,000 animals.

Recent reintroduction programmes in the parks of Zimbabwe and Mozambique, and in the Addo park of South Africa have improved the situation locally. Other populations live in the Etosha national park in Namibia, in Somalia, Chad, Uganda and Zaire.

Although the black rhino is smaller than the white rhino, it has the reputation of being more aggressive, particularly towards humans. Many African adventure stories feature a black rhino charging an intrepid hunter who bravely dispatches the 'enraged beast' with his gun. The myth of the black rhino's aggression is based on a half-truth: while an animal will always charge at an intruder (even another rhino) the charge is not an attack but a display. The animal will either veer off to one side, or stop the charge at a few feet from the victim.

UNDER THREAT

RHINOCEROS FAMILY

As the 21st century approaches, the future of the entire rhinoceros family hangs in the balance. While the calls for conservation become louder, so the determination of poachers grows ever stronger, fuelled by the increasing value of the plunder from their kills.

Rhinos have long suffered at the hands of man. In Asia, hunting has gradually reduced population levels to mere remnants of their former size. The Sumatran rhinoceros now numbers around 150 animals, scattered through South-east Asia. The Indian species probably totals 1500, confined to a handful of reserves in India and Nepal. Most grim is the plight of the Javan rhino, now restricted to a single reserve on the island - just 50 animals are left.

The picture is slightly better for the two African species; but it is worsening at an alarming rate. In the southern part of its range the white rhino was brought to the brink of extinction during the last century. Since then concerted conservation efforts have pulled it back, but now the northern race is on the brink of extinction: a population of less than 20 animals survive in a Zairean national park. The black rhino is still the most abundant species, but its numbers have also fallen and relentless poaching is threatening it further. It now bears the greatest share of the hunting pressure.

It is the rhino's horn which has brought about the animal's tragic downfall. Powdered rhino horn is traditionally used as an aphrodisiac in parts of India, and as a relief from fever, headaches, heart and liver problems, and skin diseases in the Far East. Chemically, rhino horn is little different from the material which makes up fingernails, hooves and the hard casing of cattle and antelope horns. Scientists can find no reason why the substance should possess any special properties, and suggest that the effects attributed to it are probably psychological. But traditions are strong.

In recent years a further source of demand for rhino horn has come into prominence - one that threatens to be even more potent in its effect on rhino numbers. In North Yemen, daggers furnished with handles of rhino horn are a prized status symbol. Wealth from the oil industry has prompted a greater demand for these knives, with a resulting increase in both the trade and the value of horn.

When values are high, the rewards for poachers soon outweigh any dangers they face. Nowadays poachers must risk meeting armed gamekeepers in some parts of Africa. But even there the shoot-to-kill policy is not enough to deter hunters. If the slaughter continues unabated, the wild rhino may not even live out the 20th century.

TOP A female white rhinoceros grazes with her offspring. White rhino calves are able to follow the mother about three days after they are born.
ABOVE Two males cross horns at a territorial boundary. Such confrontation is pure ritual and may be a way of avoiding combat.
PAGE 360 Three white rhinos graze at a waterhole. The long muzzles and broad mouths of the white rhino are suitable for grazing short grasses.

The British explorer and big game hunter, Frederick Selous (1851-1917), gave one of the earliest defences of the animal: 'I do not wish to claim...that the rhinoceros is a pleasant animal, merely that it is not so irritable, irascible and dangerous as it is made out by many travellers...I personally killed over 100 rhinoceroses in eight days and can say that they are much less dangerous to hunt than lion, elephant and buffalo!'.

Like other rhinos, black rhinos deposit dung as a means of marking pathways and territory. Where there are few rhinos per hectare, the home ranges of males overlap and are not usually defended by them. Where the density of black rhino is greater, such as in the Hluhluwe-Umfolozi Reserve in South Africa, breeding males will defend territories of 400 hectares against other breeding males. However, non-breeding males are still tolerated within these areas by the resident male. Mating takes place at any time of year and is followed by a 15 month gestation. The single young, weighing 40kg at birth, lives with the mother for up to four years. Among black, white and Indian rhinos there is usually a space of two to four years before the females have another offspring. Births occur in any month.